Publisher's Note

It takes either a brave or a stupid person to reprint a 1924 rebus puzzle book without some editing. Seventy-five years ago it was considered acceptable to freely caricature non-whites in various derogatory ways. Such caricatures have been deleted from this book. Accordingly, you will often see three puzzles per page where there were originally four. We felt the gain to be greater than the loss.

Leonard G. Lee, Publisher
Ottawa
September, 2000

SAM LOYD'S

PICTURE PUZZLES

WITH

ANSWERS

PREFACE

WHEN I am asked by editors and others who wish to cater to that legion of people, young and old, who are devoted to puzzle solving—"What is the most popular form of puzzle?" I unhesitatingly reply that the rebus "picture puzzle," is the "puzzle of the populace," as it were.

Where hundreds are partial to puzzles of the mathematical and mechanical sort or to word puzzling with charades, word-squares, anagrams, conundrums, enigmas, transpositions, etc., etc.; thousands, yes, tens of thousands, are followers of the "picture puzzle." This puzzle may be described as a word or name, represented pictorially by any sort of object, peculiar arrangement of letters, numerals, etc., the spelling or pronunciation of which is similar to that of itself.

Fifty thousand people recently participated in one of my solving contests, and the puzzles that inspired this mammoth tournament of wits were of the "picture puzzle" variety, such as compose the pages of this book. A newspaper which published one of the contests received a number of replies equal to one-third of its circulation. All of which is convincing proof of the pre-eminent popularity of the "picture puzzle."

When I say that the "picture puzzle" is the puzzle of the masses, I do not wish to be understood as classifying it as of "common, or garden variety," calling for inferior calibre of intellect. True, it engages the naturally alert faculties, rather than the scholastic and scientific. At the same time, there are qualities of wit, humor and imagination exhibited in rebus solving that betoken mental radiations of the brightest rays. I have seen a college professor strain and fail for the answer to a rebus that was solved rather readily by a bright child. It proves at least, that in some mental processes the native, unskilled wit will outstrip the polished intellect of the scholar.

We must not assume that the solving of any sort of puzzle, whether it be the cracking of a riddle or the analysis of a problem in higher mathematics, is arrived at by chance or slipshod methods. A solution is gained by reasoning along straight lines; by ingenuity and cleverness; for puzzles are not solved by dullards.

There is no better mental training than puzzle solving, and the pastime must be considered more seriously than a mere fad or amusement. I firmly believe that puzzles constitute one of the greatest educational agencies in existence, and I have always treated them from this standpoint. Parents cannot too early encourage their children's love for puzzles. Mastering a problem through the force of his own reasoning power will imbue a child with pride and self-reliance that act like a tonic on his intellectual growth.

The brightest man of my acquaintance is the manager of a newspaper, who, plucked from school at thirteen years of age, frankly attributes the splendidly trained mind he now possesses to his passionate devotion to puzzles, which set in after his formal schooling. He has the quickest head for figures I have ever encountered, and his brilliant reasoning powers are along the direct and original lines of the puzzle solver.

The peculiar fascination that lies in puzzle solving is no enigma. Human nature is inquisitive, and will spare no effort in probing for the solution of a mystery. Every thinking person experiences keen satisfaction when a perplexing puzzle has been mastered. "Eureka! I met the puzzle and the answer is mine." A puzzle is an impish challenge to our wits—"Let's see you guess me." "You bet I will;" and the tussle is on. There we have full explanation of the charm that this ancient pastime holds for most of us.

In working out the puzzles in the following pages, reference to geography, history, English, zoology, and other sources of book information is constant; and thus educational and instructive as well as entertaining. The exercise is of inestimable value to the young folks, who are unconsciously storing up useful knowledge while pursuing their labor of love.

Answers to all of the puzzles are contained in the back pages of the book, but it is to be hoped that this information will not be prematurely sought. Don't look up the answer until you have worked out what you consider must be the correct solution.

SAM LOYD.

Brooklyn, N. Y.

REBUS BOYS

The familiar Christian names of four boys are represented by the sketches. It is more than likely that these fellows are among your friends.

PUZZLING CHEESES

Each of the pictures suggests the name of a well-known kind of cheese. Two are of imported varieties, and the other two grandma knows how to make.

PUZZLES FROM THE ZOO

Four wild quadrupeds are represented in this group of rebus sketches. One is a great favorite at the menagerie and another is a mean and skulking fellow.

BEDROOM PUZZLES

These sketches are illustrative of four things that greeted the artist's eye as he stepped into an attractive and comfortable bedroom.

4

ARBOREAL REBUSES

The puzzle artist, strolling through the park with his sketch book, found four trees that are here transplanted in the rebus garden.

JUICY PUZZLES

Four kinds of luscious fruit are here pictured in rebus form. Two of them grow on trees, another on a vine and the fourth on a bush.

A GOOD GIRL PUZZLE

We know a little miss who possesses so many admirable
traits, or features, that it was no puzzle at all to select four
of her good points for rebus illustration.

IN THE GOLDEN WEST

Each picture represents the name of a city, town or village to be found on the map of California. One of the places is named after an American poet.

A PUZZLING TICKER

The inside of a watch is a puzzle to most of us, but the names of its principal parts are well known. Each rebus represents one of those parts.

9

MARYLAND TOWNS

Each picture represents the name of a city, town or village to be found on the map of Maryland.

A CHRISTMAS ZOO

A little zoologist's Christmas list will make his tree look like our sketch if all his wishes for animal toys come true. How many creatures can you find?

IOWA TOWNS

Each picture represents the name of a city, town or village to be found on the map of the State of Iowa.

ALABAMA TOWNS

Each picture represents the name of a city, town or village to be found on the map of Alabama. One of the places is named after a Greek city.

13

COLORADO TOWNS

Each picture represents the name of a city, town or village to be found on the map of the State of Colorado.

REBUSES FROM THE SEA

Here are three rebus fish that you are challenged to snare with your wits. Two you should catch easily, but the third is a game fellow, hard to land.

15

WASHINGTON'S GENERALS

You are challenged to translate the rebus sketches into the surnames of four generals who gained fame under our great hero's leadership.

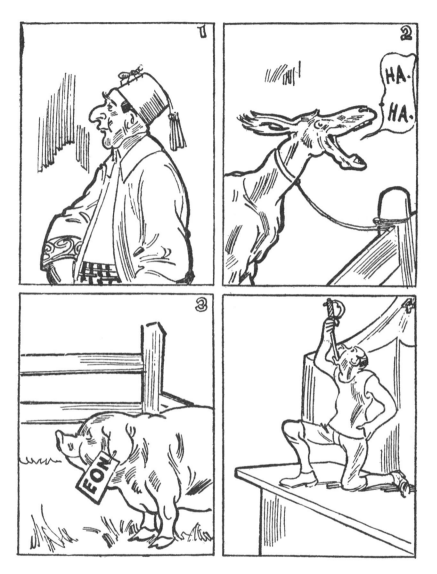

FLYING REBUSES

Each sketch represents the name of a bird. The dictionary says that one of them is a large Australian insectivorous kingfisher.

TOURING WISCONSIN

Each picture represents the name of a city, town or village to be found on the map of Wisconsin.

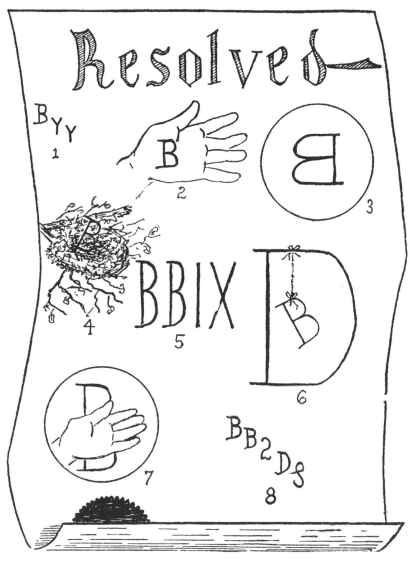

NEW YEAR'S RESOLUTIONS

Here are eight rebus resolutions for the New Year that, if carried out, will make a fellow's conduct about ninety-nine per cent perfect.

FLORAL REBUSES

In this rebus garden you are invited to pluck the names of four flowers. Even if you are not up in horticulture you have often heard of these blossoms.

REBUS RIVERS

The names of three well-known rivers of North America are here represented. One of them, named after its discoverer, is majestically beautiful.

PUZZLES ON THE WING

This page deals with members of the feathered tribe. The names of four well-known birds are represented by the rebus pictures.

REBUSES DOWN IN MAINE

Turn to your atlas and scan the big New England State for the names of four cities, towns or villages that will fit the four pictures.

REBUS GIRLS

The Christian names of four girls are here presented in rebus form. One is a good, old-fashioned Southern name, and the most difficult to guess.

CHRISTMAS TREE REBUSES

Here we have in rebus form, four gifts that hung on our Christmas tree. No. 1 for big Tom, No. 2 for Miss Alice, No. 3 for Grandpa and No. 4 for little Bob.

25

WASHINGTON TOWNS

Each of the sketches represents the name of a city, town or village to be found on the map of the State of Washington.

MICHIGAN REBUSES

Each of the sketches represents the name of a city, town or village to be found on the map of the State of Michigan.

AT THE MENAGERIE

Four creatures at the zoo posed for these rebus pictures. If you can capture all four it must be admitted that you are a good puzzle hunter.

REBUSES FROM THE SOIL

As the truck farmer proudly escorted us through his rows
and patches of flourishing plants, we noted four of the hardy
vegetables that are here served up as rebuses.

ARIZONA TOWNS

Each picture represents the name of a city, town or village to be found on the map of the State of Arizona.

AUTOMOBILE PUZZLES

We are all more or less familiar with the anatomy of the "gasoline horse," so let us see who can identify these four automobile parts in rebus form.

A PUZZLING GOOD BOY

Of the many fine qualities to look for in a manly boy here are four of his best points translated into rebus form.

CLOTHED IN REBUSES

Among the puzzles associated with a woman are the enigmatical features of her clothing. Each of the sketches represents some part of a woman's frock.

FEMININE PUZZLES

The names of four sorts of dress-goods are here depicted in rebus guise. One is a humble material and the other three of pretentious weave.

CRAWLING PUZZLES

The names of four insects of well-known species are here presented in rebus form. Three of them you will probably guess off-hand but the other is hard to catch.

LOUISIANA TOWNS

Each picture represents the name of a city, town or village to be found on the map of the State of Louisiana.

PUZZLING ANATOMY

The class in physiology will now come to attention, so that we may see who can discover the four parts of the human body represented by the sketches.

IN OLD KENTUCKY

Each picture represents the name of a city, town or village to be found on the map of the State of Kentucky.

PUZZLING PRESIDENTS

The surnames of four ex-Presidents of the United States are represented by these pictures. This is a good time to read over the full list.

STATES AND COUNTRIES

What four states and countries do these pictures represent? One is of a nation that played a most heroic part in the World's War.

BUDDY'S DINNER PARTY

Buddy went to a party the other night and had many good things to eat. Here are four of the dishes that he asked for second helpings of.

BUILDING ACCESSORIES

As we paused to watch the building of a new bungalow, some of the articles scattered about provided us with four subjects for this page.

"LONE STAR" PUZZLES

Each picture represents the name of a city, town or village to be found on the map of the State of Texas.

VERMONT REBUSES

Each sketch represents a place to be found on the map of Vermont. Don't forget that for rebus purposes the little places are as important as big towns.

A PUZZLING BOUQUET

As we strolled through my host's garden I mentally plucked a blossom here and there for the puzzle book. Each of the rebuses represents a well-known flower.

REBUS VEHICLES

Each picture represents the name of an old-fashioned horse-drawn vehicle. Granddad will help you out with these if you are too modern.

PASTRY PUZZLES

Each of the rebuses represents a sort of cake with which we are all familiar. They will make your mouth water after you guess them.

47

MINNESOTA TOWNS

Study the map of the State of Minnesota and you should be able to locate four places whose names will nicely fit these four sketches.

THE EMPIRE STATE

Each of the sketches represents a city, town or village in the State of New York. In scanning the map don't fail to take in Long Island.

CONFECTIONERY PUZZLES

Four sorts of popular candy are to be found in these pictures. Two are of the old-fashioned kind, and the other two more up to date.

THE ARTIST'S PUZZLES

"Why shouldn't my palette provide some good puzzle material?" said the artist. And so it did, for each of the sketches represents a color I found there.

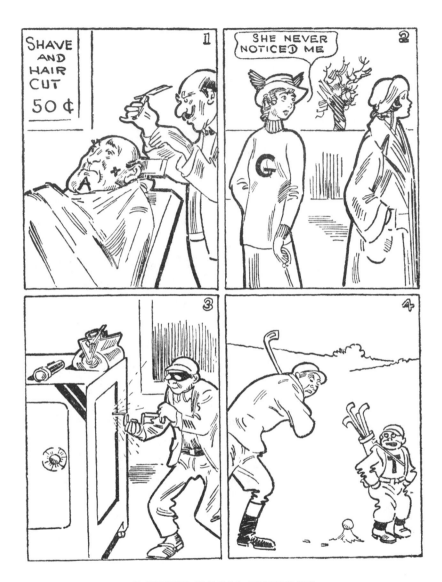

DINING-ROOM PUZZLES

Each of the pictures represents something appropriate to the dining-room. Not articles of food, but items of furniture and ware.

RANKING OFFICERS

In a photograph taken during a famous Frenchman's visit to West Point appears four officers of different ranks. Those four commissions are here represented.

CONNECTICUT REBUSES

Each sketch represents the name of a place to be found on the map of the "Nutmeg State."

TOURING KANSAS

The names of four places to be found on the map of Kansas are here presented in rebus form. Scrutinize the map well and you will surely find them.

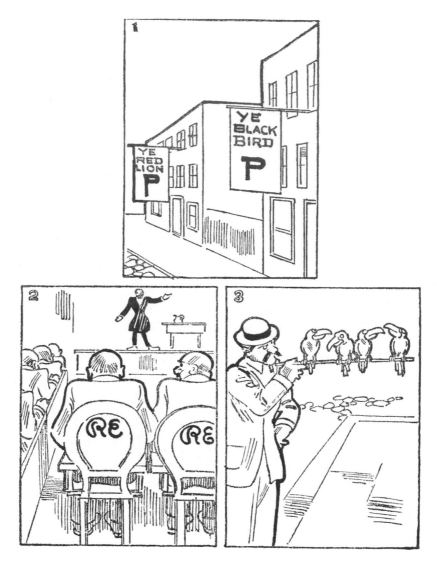

IN A LADY'S HANDBAG

The three little rebuses represent articles that one would be almost sure to find in the average woman's handbag. What are they?

IN A BOY'S POCKET

As Johnny's teacher emptied his pockets several articles came to view that furnish good puzzle material. Each picture represents one of Johnny's treasures.

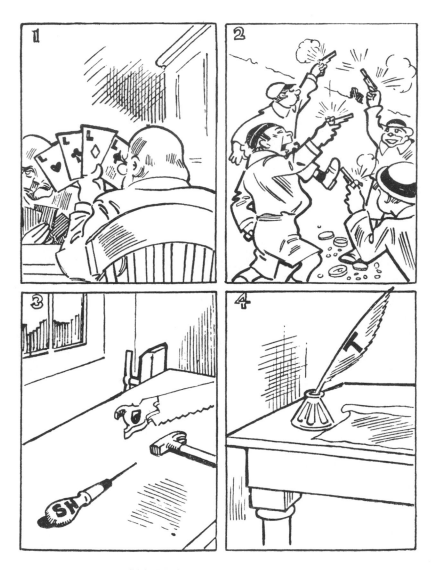

IN GRANDMA'S TRUNK

On a rainy day the children invaded the garret and rummaged through Grandma's trunk. Each of the pictures represents something that was brought to view.

PUZZLES ON FOOT

Footwear furnishes the subject for this page, so we are expected to find in each of the little pictures the name of a familiar footcovering.

SPICY PUZZLES

This page of rebuses might be called highly flavored, for each of the four represents a well-known spice with a snappy flavor.

PUZZLING COIFFURES

Four young ladies issued from the hair-dresser's studio, and the four styles in which their locks were arranged are set forth in the sketches.

PENNSYLVANIA TOWNS

Cast your eye over the map of the Keystone State and you should be able to discover the names of the three places represented by the sketches.

62

CACKLING PUZZLES

We are all familiar with the names of popular barnyard fowl, so should have little difficulty in guessing the breeds of chickens here represented.

LIVING-ROOM PUZZLES

Each of the four pictures, in a rebus way, stands for something that we are sure to encounter in the living-room of a comfortable home.

AMBITION PUZZLES

Here we have the replies of three girls who were asked what careers they were ambitious to follow. Each picture represents an occupation.

IN FATHER'S POCKET

Bobby climbed on Daddy's knee and investigated his inside coat pocket. Four of the things he discovered are represented by the sketches.

KITCHEN PUZZLES

Step into any well-appointed kitchen and you'll be almost sure to find there the four things represented by the sketches.

MASSACHUSETTS TOWNS

In a tour of the Bay State we passed through four places whose names provided subjects for this group of rebus sketches. Can you guess them?

MOTORING IN NEW JERSEY

Each of the sketches represents a town, village or city that we culled from the sign-boards while touring the State of New Jersey.

DECLARATION FATHERS

Each of the sketches represents the surname of a signer of the Declaration of Independence. Now we shall have to get out our history books.

AMERICAN INDIANS

Each sketch represents the name of a well-known tribe of American Indians.

SCHOOL DAYS

Four school studies that boys and girls will all have to wrestle with, if they are not already so engaged, can be found in these four pictures.

OHIO TOWNS

You will find on the map of Ohio four names of towns, villages or cities that have been translated into these four rebus sketches.

WEAPONS OF WAR

Let us hope that the nations will never again take up against one another such weapons as are here represented—for then there would be no more wars.

BEANS A LA REBUS

The humble bean, in its various forms, provides good puzzle diet, so let us see who can discover the four species here served in rebus form.

EQUINE PUZZLES

A cowboy calls his mount a bronco, or perhaps a mustang. Then there are other names for our friend the horse. Translate each sketch into a class of horses.

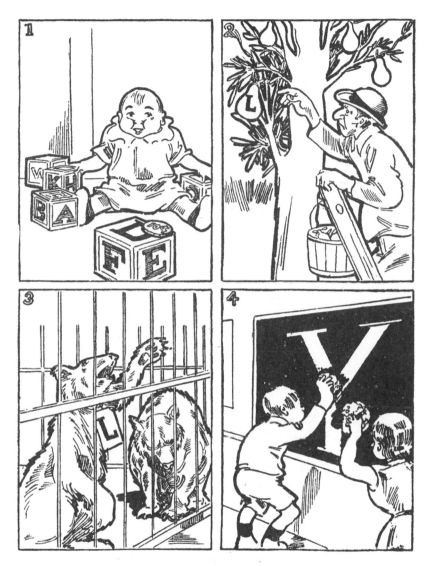

PUZZLE GEMS

Each of the sketches represents the name of a precious stone that one is likely to see in any high-class jeweler's window; and perhaps you possess all four of them.

PUZZLES AT THE GROCERY

Here are pictured in rebus form three articles that you could surely find at the corner grocery shop.

OUTDOOR SPORTS

Each of the sketches represents the name of a well-known outdoor game. Even if you are not of the athletic type you have often heard of these four sports.

DRESS-GOODS PUZZLES

When mother was getting the girls' dresses ready for vacation days, she used four sorts of material that are here presented in rebus form.

PUZZLING VEGETABLES

Each of the pictures represents the name of a vegetable of the "common, or garden variety." Two are of the same family.

PUZZLES OVERHEAD

Various sorts of headwear for men and women are here depicted in puzzle guise, each of the four sketches being decipherable into the name of a hat.

PUZZLING INSECTS

Strolling about the country in vacation days, you are almost sure to encounter the insects represented by these pictures. Can you name them?

PUZZLING GIRLS

We selected a group of little girls to pose for this page. Each of the pictures represents a very pretty Christian feminine name.

PUZZLING OCCUPATIONS

I asked four boys what occupations they were going to follow, and their answers made good rebus puzzles. Each picture represents some trade, profession or calling.

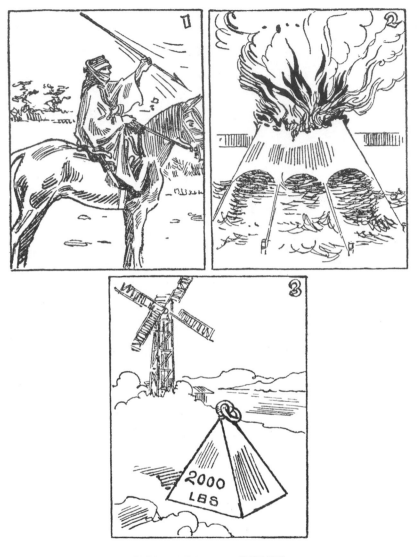

POETICAL PUZZLES

Even if you are not a lover of poetry, yet you must have often heard the names of the world-famous poets represented by these pictures.

CIVIL WAR GENERALS

Each of the four sketches represents in a rebus way the surname of a distinguished General who fought for the Blue or the Gray.

HEADY PUZZLES

Each of the pictures represents some feature to be found on or in one's head. That, of course, includes the face, or any part above the neck.

REBUS CAPITALS

Each of the pictures represents the name of a Capital city of the United States. Too few of us are able to name offhand all of the Capitals.

REBUS BOYS

The Christian names of four boys are here presented in rebus form. They're good, democratic names, without flourish.

SHIP AHOY PUZZLES

Each of the pictures represents some sort of craft, large or small, that man has fashioned for navigating the waters. You have heard of them all.

AT THE DRYGOODS SHOP

When mother returned from her shopping tour, the children found in her parcels the four articles here depicted in rebus dress.

THANKSGIVING DINNER

Each of the sketches represents something especially appropriate for the Thanksgiving dinner. The four together would make a satisfactory repast.

PUZZLING CANINES

The names of four familiar breeds of dogs are represented by the pictures. They are not of the fashionable world, but are of the staunch and useful types.

PUZZLING FRUIT

Each of the four sketches suggests the name of a luscious fruit. Three are fairly easy to guess, but the fourth will stump the average puzzler.

PUZZLING ORCHESTRA

Each of the pictures represents the name of a well-known musical instrument. To play upon two of them requires good lung power.

AN ANIMAL HUNT

Each of the pictures represents the name of some wild animal. It is more than likely that all four are boarding at the nearest Zoo.

HARDWARE PUZZLES

Each of the pictures represents some article to be found on the shelves of the hardware shop. Nos. 2, 3 and 4 should not take you long, but No. 1 is a sticker.

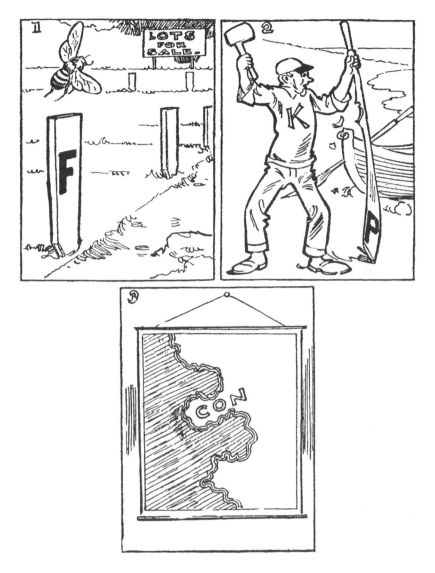

MEATY PUZZLES

A peek into the butcher boy's basket provided subjects for this page. What three kinds of meat can you find represented in the pictures?

MARKET BASKET PUZZLES

When the good wife opened her market basket the first four things that came to view provided subjects for these rebus sketches. What are they?

ABBREVIATED STATES

Each of the pictures represents a word which corresponds to the abbreviated form of spelling one of the United States of America.

PUZZLES FROM THE WOODS

Each of the sketches represents the name of a familiar tree. The four are natives of North America and are frequently seen growing together.

HISSING PUZZLES

Each of the pictures represents the name of some well-known reptile. Each is a venomous fellow whose sting would mean almost sure death.

FINNY PUZZLES

The puzzle man went fishing for this group of rebuses. Each picture represents the name of a familiar fish. How many of the four can you land?

REBUSES IN BLOOM

Here is a rebus nosegay, composed of four beautiful flowers. How many of the buds can you pluck?

ARKANSAS TOWNS

Each picture represents the name of a city, town or village to be found on the map of Arkansas.

ANSWERS TO THE PICTURE PUZZLES

Corresponding to the Numbered Pages

Page

1. REBUS BOYS—
1. Isaac. 2. Paul. 3. Oscar. 4. Roland.

2. PUZZLING CHEESES—
1. Edam. 2. Roquefort. 3. Cream. 4. Pot-cheese.

3. PUZZLES FROM THE ZOO—
1. Eland. 2. Elephant. 3. Hyena. 4. Tapir.

4. BEDROOM PUZZLES—
1. Dresser. 2. Scarf. 3. Tick. 4. Brush.

5. ARBOREAL REBUSES—
1. Dogwood. 2. Rubber. 3. Ash. 4. Palm.

6. JUICY PUZZLES—
1. Alligator Pear. 2. Grapes. 3. Cherries. 4. Currants.

7. A GOOD GIRL PUZZLE—
1. Grace. 2. Beauty. 3. Charity. 4. Pride.

8. IN THE GOLDEN WEST—
1. Stockton. 2. Hayward. 3. Longbeach. 4. Whittier.

9. A PUZZLING TICKER—
1. Hairspring. 2. Minute hand. 3. Dial. 4. Wheels.

10. MARYLAND TOWNS—
1. Hurlock. 2. Snow Hill. 3. North East. 4. Westernport.

11. A CHRISTMAS ZOO—
Cat, Squirrel, Parrot, Giraffe, Armadillo, Anteater, Crocodile, Tortoise, Zebu, Toucan, Deer, Seal, Ape, Penguin, Porcupine, Dachshund, Camel, Hyena, Bear, Elephant, Owl, Hippopotamus, Eagle, Rhinoceros, Lion, Cow, Leopard, Kangaroo, Sloth, Ostrich, Zebra, Tiger, Rabbit, Buffalo, Horse, Goat, Pig—37.

ANSWERS TO THE PICTURE PUZZLES

12. IOWA TOWNS—
1. Atlantic. 2. Cascade. 3. Logan. 4. Tipton.

13. ALABAMA TOWNS—
1. Athens. 2. Florala. 3. Headland. 4. Lanett.

14. COLORADO TOWNS—
1. Brush. 2. Manitou. 3. Victor. 4. Lamar.

15. REBUSES FROM THE SEA—
1. Herring. 2. Scup. 3. Star.

16. WASHINGTON'S GENERALS—
1. Stark. 2. Morgan. 3. Wayne. 4. Gates (gay eights).

17. FLYING REBUSES—
1. Pheasant. 2. Laughing jackass. 3. Pigeon. 4. Swallow.

18. TOURING WISCONSIN—
1. Appleton. 2. Beaver Dam. 3. Brodhead. 4. Milwaukee.

19. NEW YEAR'S RESOLUTIONS—
1. Be wise. 2. Be on hand. 3. Be backward in nothing.
4. Be honest. 5. Be benign. 6. Be independent. 7. Be
behindhand in naught. 8. Be studious.

20. FLORAL REBUSES—
1. Dandelion. 2. Foxglove. 3. Orchid. 4. Lady's Slipper.

21. REBUS RIVERS—
1. Hudson. 2. White River. 3. Suwanee.

22. PUZZLES ON THE WING—
1. Condor. 2. Starling. 3. Nightingale. 4. Toucan.

23. REBUSES DOWN IN MAINE—
1. Bar Harbor. 2. Deering. 3. Bath. 4. Belfast.

24. REBUS GIRLS—
1. Hattie. 2. Kate. 3. Lucy (loose C). 4. Mandy (man D).

25. CHRISTMAS TREE REBUSES—
1. Watch fob. 2. Stationery. 3. Cane. 4. Wheel barrow.

ANSWERS TO THE PICTURE PUZZLES

Page

26. WASHINGTON TOWNS—
1. Walla Walla. 2. Seattle. 3. Spokane.

27. MICHIGAN REBUSES—
1. Caro. 2. Marquette. 3. Ionia. 4. Marine.

28. AT THE MENAGERIE—
1. Cayman. 2. Wolf. 3. Sloth. 4. Lynx.

29. REBUSES FROM THE SOIL—
1. Corn (corps N). 2. Squash. 3. Leeks. 4. Turnips.

30. ARIZONA TOWNS—
1. Globe. 2. Flagstaff. 3. Metcalf. 4. Tombstone.

31. AUTOMOBILE PUZZLES—
1. Hood. 2. Battery. 3. Carbureter. 4. Crank shaft.

32. A PUZZLING GOOD BOY—
1. Honesty (on ST). 2. Common sense (cents).
3. Courage (curage). 4. Uprightness.

33. CLOTHED IN REBUSES—
1. Waist. 2. Sleeves. 3. Lining.

34. FEMININE PUZZLES—
1. Silk. 2. Charmeuse. 3. Crepe. 4. Gingham.

35. CRAWLING PUZZLES—
1. Caterpillar. 2. Beetle. 3. Darning Needle. 4. Scorpion.

36. LOUISIANA TOWNS—
1. Rayne. 2. Homer. 3. White Castle. 4. Amite.

37. PUZZLING ANATOMY—
1. Arms. 2. Chest. 3. Veins. 4. Two feet.

38. IN OLD KENTUCKY—
1. Burnside. 2. Eminence. 3. Wayland. 4. Carlisle.

39. PUZZLING PRESIDENTS—
1. Washington. 2. Taylor. 3. Adams. 4. Garfield.

40. STATES AND COUNTRIES—
1. Belgium. 2. Wales. 3. Cuba. 4. Tennessee.

ANSWERS TO THE PICTURE PUZZLES

41. BUDDY'S DINNER PARTY—
    1. Pumpkin. 2. Potatoes. 3. Candies (cannedEE).
    4. Cabinet pudding.

42. BUILDING ACCESSORIES—
    1. Bells (belles). 2. Spade. 3. Carpenter's tools (two LL).
    4. Glass.

43. "LONE STAR" PUZZLES—
    1. Ennis. 2. Longview. 3. Ranger. 4. Temple.

44. VERMONT REBUSES—
    1. Highgate. 2. Bellows Falls. 3. Barnet. 4. Orwell.

45. A PUZZLING BOUQUET—
    1. Orchid. 2. Jonquil. 3. Pansy.

46. REBUS VEHICLES—
    1. Cart. 2. Hack. 3. Sulky. 4. Shay.

47. PASTRY PUZZLES—
    1. Lady Fingers. 2. Marble (cake). 3. Citron (sit run).
    4. Pound (cake).

48. MINNESOTA TOWNS—
    1. Cannon Falls. 2. Bird Island. 3. Melrose. 4. Blackduck.

49. THE EMPIRE STATE—
    1. Buffalo. 2. Catskill. 3. Cohoes. 4. Sea Cliff.

50. CONFECTIONERY PUZZLES—
    1. Kisses. 2. Butter Scotch. 3. Bon Bons.
    4. Molasses Candy.

51. THE ARTIST'S PUZZLE—
    1. Yellow. 2. Blue. 3. Pink. 4. Red (read).

52. DINING-ROOM PUZZLES—
    1. China. 2. Cut Glass. 3. Sideboard. 4. Tea Caddy.

53. RANKING OFFICERS—
    1. Captain. 2. Marshal. 3. Lieutenant (loot ten ant).
    4. Colonel.

ANSWERS TO THE PICTURE PUZZLES

Page

54. CONNECTICUT REBUSES—
1. Essex. 2. Derby. 3. Orange. 4. Enfield.

55. TOURING KANSAS—
1. Ellinwood. 2. Liberal. 3. Great Bend. 4. Parsons.

56. IN A LADY'S HANDBAG—
1. Pins. 2. Receipts. 3. Bills.

57. IN A BOY'S POCKET—
1. Top. 2. Marbles. 3. String. 4. Pennies.

58. IN GRANDMA'S TRUNK—
1. Laces. 2. Caps. 3. Shawl. 4. Quilt.

59. PUZZLES—ON FOOT—
1. Slippers. 2. Shoes. 3. Pumps. 4. Sandals.

60. SPICY PUZZLES—
1. Capers. 2. Ginger. 3. Cloves. 4. Allspice.

61. PUZZLING COIFFURES—
1. Bobbed. 2. Bangs. 3. Curled. 4. Waves.

62. PENNSYLVANIA TOWNS—
1. Warren. 2. Freeland. 3. High Spire.

63. CACKLING PUZZLES—
1. Barred Plymouth Rock. 2. Wyandotte. 3. Cochin China.

64. LIVING-ROOM PUZZLES—
1. Lamp. 2. Cabinet. 3. Easy chair. 4. Couch.

65. AMBITION PUZZLES—
1. Saleswoman. 2. Milliner. 3. Actress.

66. IN FATHER'S POCKET—
1. Stock. 2. Checks. 3. Fountain pen. 4. Notes.

67. KITCHEN PUZZLES—
1. Range. 2. Pantry. 3. Broom. 4. Tinware.

68. MASSACHUSETTS TOWNS—
1. Concord. 2. Gardner. 3. Hyannis. 4. Manchester.

ANSWERS TO THE PICTURE PUZZLES

69. MOTORING IN NEW JERSEY—
1. Hackensack. 2. Long Branch. 3. Camden. 4. Newark.

70. DECLARATION FATHERS—
1. Clymer. 2. Chase. 3. Paine. 4. Smith.

71. AMERICAN INDIANS—
1. Crow. 2. Blackfoot. 3. Apache. 4. Pawnee.

72. SCHOOL DAYS—
1. Reading. 2. English. 3. Penmanship. 4. Mathematics.

73. OHIO TOWNS—
1. Barnhill. 2. Campbell. 3. Dayton. 4. Hanging Rock.

74. WEAPONS OF WAR—
1. Bayonet. 2. Cannon. 3. Mortar. 4. Revolver.

75. BEANS A LA REBUS—
1. Kidney. 2. Lima. 3. String. 4. Wax.

76. EQUINE PUZZLES—
1. Cob. 2. Cayuse. 3. Filly. 4. Hunter.

77. PUZZLE GEMS—
1. Diamond. 2. Pearl. 3. Beryl. 4. Ruby.

78. PUZZLES AT THE GROCERY—
1. Tomatoes. 2. Butter. 3. Salt.

79. OUTDOOR SPORTS—
1. La crosse. 2. Lawn tennis. 3. Golf. 4. Football.

80. DRESS-GOODS PUZZLES—
1. Satin. 2. Muslin. 3. Cotton. 4. Linen.

81. PUZZLING VEGETABLES—
1. Spinach. 2. Beans. 3. Cauliflower. 4. Cabbage.

82. PUZZLES OVERHEAD—
1. Bonnet. 2. Toque. 3. Beaver. 4. Round sailor.

83. PUZZLING INSECTS—
1. Butterflies. 2. Dragonflies. 3. Hornet.

ANSWERS TO THE PICTURE PUZZLES

84. PUZZLING GIRLS—
    1. Rose. 2. Dora. 3. Pansy. 4. Mary (mare E).

85. PUZZLING OCCUPATIONS—
    1. Carpenters. 2. Chauffeurs. 3. Grocer. 4. Architect.

86. POETICAL PUZZLES—
    1. Shakespeare. 2. Burns. 3. Milton.

87. CIVIL WAR GENERALS—
    1. Grant. 2. Hood. 3. Butler. 4. Wheeler.

88. HEADY PUZZLES—
    1. Lash. 2. Palate. 3. Pupils. 4. Temple.

89. REBUS CAPITALS—
    1. Boise. 2. Richmond. 3. Annapolis. 4. Columbus.

90. REBUS BOYS—
    1. Henry. 2. Carl. 3. Peter (pea eater). 4. James.

91. SHIP AHOY PUZZLES—
    1. Cutter. 2. Ark. 3. Bark. 4. Yawl.

92. AT THE DRY GOODS SHOP—
    1. Aprons. 2. Needles (need L's). 3. Braid. 4. Hose.

93. THANKSGIVING DINNER—
    1. Celery. 2. Mince pie. 3. Turkey. 4. Cranberries.

94. PUZZLING CANINES—
    1. Pointer. 2. Pug. 3. Great Dane. 4. Bull.

95. PUZZLING FRUIT—
    1. Blackberries. 2. Peaches (P chess). 3. Pears. 4. Dates.

96. PUZZLING ORCHESTRA—
    1. Cornet. 2. Lyre. 3. Cymbals (symbols). 4. Bugle.

97. AN ANIMAL HUNT—
    1. Groundhog. 2. Weasel. 3. Monkey. 4. Mongoose.

98. HARDWARE PUZZLES—
    1. White lead. 2. Nails. 3. Casters. 4. Locks.

ANSWERS TO THE PICTURE PUZZLES

99. MEATY PUZZLES—
   1. Beef steak. 2. Pork chops (P oar K chops). 3. Bacon.

100. MARKET BASKET PUZZLES—
   1. Starch. 2. Ceylon tea. 3. Thyme. 4. Molasses.

101. ABBREVIATED STATES—
   1. Miss. 2. Ill. 3. Pa. 4. Ore.

102. PUZZLES FROM THE WOODS—
   1. Pine. 2. Maple. 3. Fir. 4. Spruce.

103. HISSING PUZZLES—
   1. Copperhead. 2. Adder. 3. Rattle.

104. FINNY PUZZLES—
   1. Sheepshead. 2. Skate. 3. Minnow. 4. Cuttle.

105. REBUSES IN BLOOM—
   1. Peony (P on knee). 2. Tulip (tool IP). 3. Sweet peas.
   4. Dog rose.

106. ARKANSAS TOWNS—
   1. Marked Tree. 2. Mena 3. Ozark.

THIS PUZZLE, IN COLORS, IS A SUPPLEMENT TO
THE BOOK

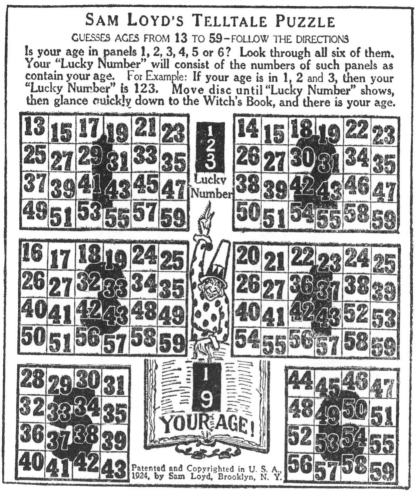

SAM LOYD'S TELLTALE PUZZLE

GUESSES AGES FROM 13 TO 59 — FOLLOW THE DIRECTIONS

Is your age in panels 1, 2, 3, 4, 5 or 6? Look through all six of them. Your "Lucky Number" will consist of the numbers of such panels as contain your age. For Example: If your age is in 1, 2 and 3, then your "Lucky Number" is 123. Move disc until "Lucky Number" shows, then glance quickly down to the Witch's Book, and there is your age.

Patented and Copyrighted in U. S. A., 1924, by Sam Loyd, Brooklyn, N. Y.

Here's a Puzzle to Work Out on Your "Telltale Puzzle" Card

"TOM, DICK AND HARRY"

The combined ages of Tom, Dick and Harry total 100 years, and Tom is now twice as old as Dick was when Harry was as old as Dick is now.

When you have figured out the three ages, take all of the figures contained in their combined "Lucky Numbers," as revealed in the "TELLTALE PUZZLE," and arrange them in a single, simple sum without fractions, that will add up to exactly 700. Can you do it?